The Last Rendezvous

Written By:
Charles Dudley Digges, Jr.
Started in the year of our Lord,
Nineteen Hundred Ninety Nine and extended into
the millennium year of Two Thousand.

Cover designed by Jo Butz

ABOUT THE AUTHOR

A SMALL AMOUNT OF TRIVIA,
HISTORY AND PHILOSOPHY,
FROM THE AUTHOR:

Charles was born and lived in Northern Virginia, except for a two-year tour with the United States Army. He was drafted into the Army in 1966 and spent a year in Vietnam. Arriving in Vietnam a private, he received two purple hearts for being wounded twice and became Sergeant (E-5). After his return to the United States and while stationed at Fort Campbell, Kentucky, he was offered Staff Sergeant (E-6) and a bonus check for reenlistment. Being almost guaranteed a return trip to Vietnam; he declined the offer and left the military. His jobs through the years have included a farm hand, bee attendant, food store attendant for A& P Tea Company, food store Assistant Produce Manager for A&P, and bowling alley attendant. He also delivered newspapers. In his spare time he has restored and made furniture as a hobby as well as for profit. Through the years he has also been a mason, a carpenter, a deputy sheriff, and has been working for the United States Government for approximately 30 years. He and his family resided in Virginia until June of 1995, when he and his wife moved to their present home in the Pocono Mountains. They have a daughter in Massachusetts and a son in Virginia. A lover of the outdoors Charles has always been a hunter and a fisherman. He is also skilled in the arts of the Mountain Man, especially tomahawk and knife throwing.

Charles spent his childhood living and working on farms. Even during summer vacations he visited with grandparents who also lived and worked on farms.

Charles worked on farms owned by the president of Ford Motor Company where his father was the foreman, principally raising Hereford show cattle for money. The farm raised crops for the animals and supported itself. There were also horses, goats, sheep, geese, chickens, and rabbits, with each farm having streams and ponds for water. Each farm was different and had its own unique way, one being in the mountains and the other located in the flat lands. Charles learned many things from growing up on a farm that were not available to most children. His experiences developed in him the judgement to solve problems and make common sense decisions.

Charles has one younger brother, born after they moved off the farm and while they lived close to Bull Run near Manassas, Virginia. Their father worked part time on a farm near their home at Bull Run for his half-brother, tending the green houses and working with bees. The farms main occupations were developing flowers and selling honey to a company called Monarch.

Charles believes that not always having the things one wants makes one appreciate them more when they become available. One becomes more adaptable, relying on imagination. Many items needed throughout life can be created rather than store bought, and in many cases the product made by hand will outlast the store-bought item. Using one's ingenuity is a tremendous help in making anything work, whether the design started from scratch or one already knew the outcome of the finished product. Now relax and enjoy this tale of the Last Rendezvous as told by a modern day Mountain Man.

CREDITS

The descriptive and detailed illustrations throughout this book were hand drawn and appropriately placed by my extremely talented, loving and supportive wife, Katherine.

I would also like to thank my wife Katherine, Mrs. Vera Watkins from Virginia and Mrs. Providence Billings from the state of New York for their devoted time given to the editing of this book.

CONTENTS

INTRODUCTION

This story is fictional, but includes facts and actual events, which occurred in the making of a Mountain Man. Through many hours, days and years much truth was revealed and retained, and has been transferred to this amazingly informative book.

Not All Mountain Men were made this way or were required to use this method, but each Mountain Man had to establish his own creed. This tale is about an Easterner just looking for something different. It relates to many things that happened during this era and has to do with some of the ways of life, that were dealt with by him and his family. It explains some of the hardships they encountered, and the rugged struggle for their survival, in their new surroundings, while making history.

Many years ago, when the rivers ran clear and free of modern day pollution, without waste continually being emptied into them, there was a breed of humans we called the Mountain Men. These men mainly lived and stayed in the untamed territories of the western plains and the western mountainous areas. The years from

Seventeen Hundred through Eighteen Hundred and Forty seemed to be an accelerated time in history. The spread of civilization in all directions over the land, contributed to the end of the mountain man era. The individual who earned the respect to be called a Mountain Man was cut from a rough and hardy breed of men. These men knew no fear of man or beast, and their social creed was unlike any other during that period of time.

CHAPTER ONE
GROWING UP AS A COAL MINER

John was born to Sean and Molly O'Donnel in the gorgeous Delaware Water Gap, Pennsylvania. The day was Wednesday, the twenty fifth of April, Eighteen Hundred and Ten. As one looks back through history the date had no particular significance. There was not a cloud in the sky. The sun was shining brightly and gave a prism effect through droplets of water on the green grass, still wet from a fresh spring shower. Everything glistened as the sun's morning rays projected many fabulous sunburst colors, dancing and darting throughout this beautiful setting, against a backdrop of mountains. Many of the spring flowers with their array of vivid bright colors were in full bloom. The fog was slowly rising from the Delaware River as the clear water crested fully against its banks. The beautiful winding river was almost spilling over from an abundance of the mountain springs' water and the recent spring shower. Everything seemed to be happening all at once, causing a splendid sight, in the crisp morning mountain air, reminding everyone that spring had definitely sprung and she was as gorgeous as ever.

The Delaware Water Gap is in a picturesque part of the Poconos, with breathtaking mountains, spectacular waterfalls, deep green valleys and winding rivers. While admiring this much beauty one is required to look upon and ponder the many miracles performed by Mother Nature. The Delaware River flows smooth and fast through this part of Pennsylvania as it constantly meanders eastward to the Atlantic Ocean.

Many changes would take place and much hard work would be required before John would visit the ocean to the East. While living with, growing up with and working with the Immigrants, John always had questions about the ocean and the seas. The stories about the immigrants' homelands and their cultures fascinated him, even though he knew very little about the part of the world where he now lived. Hopefully, many of these questions would be answered and many of them by John, himself, at a later time.

John's parents, immigrants from Ireland, settled in Pennsylvania and the family became miners, as there were no other jobs available in the area. Sean had some experience with dynamite and other explosives from his work in the mines in Ireland. The mining boss accepted him right away, and he needed no additional training for coal mining in Pennsylvania. This New World seemed to be the answer to all their needs. Being immigrants and feeling proud to be in the New World, a land of freedom, was something these people had not felt before in their lives. It was their first time to make decisions on their own, choosing their own way of life. If they had known or expected the outcome, especially what was required for them to endure, they definitely would have made different decisions. If one could predict the future, many times things would be changed to alter the outcome.

Once they found work, shelter, a place to live while working in the mines, was a requirement. The particular miners' village, where the O'Donnel's family lived, was called Shantytown. Shantytown was the typically designed mining town, laid cut in such a manner that all the immigrants houses could be constantly watched and controlled. When something was done without permission or first being cleared through the owner's committee, it was usually struck down immediately. An example would be to change the design of the house by adding special trim or by expanding the garden. These little changes had no real meaning and obviously didn't hurt anyone but it was a way the owner's kept control of their town and tenants. Naturally the boss of the miners had the largest and the best house in the town. The foreman's house was next in line, continuing down to the miners' homes. Some of the buildings in between these were the doctor's office, the company store, the mule barn, and the church.

The home for the boss was usually a ten or twelve room two- story house and finely furnished by the owners of the mine. The boss's family was usually traveling on vacation to other parts of the world, and the children were always taught in private schools far away from home. One of the reasons the boss needed such an extravagant house was to entertain the mine owner and important guests. If the owner decided to stop by at the mine or have one of his ritzy parties, a home of suitable size and opulence was needed, since the mine owners often did not live in the immediate area.

If the owner of the mine happened to live on the site where the mine was located, his home would have resembled a mansion in size.

Throughout history wealth has been something to flaunt and poverty a source of shame. Being poor is certainly not a sin, but it restricts many of the activities requiring money and inevitably segregates mankind, causing an unseen barrier between people.

Usually, the owners of the mine did not live in the immediate area, and definitely were not required to be present for the operation to function. They and the stockholders would rely strictly on the boss for keeping the mine operational. Sometimes the owners were linked to and made up an organization or a company that was backed with large sums of money. Many important, but unknown investors would stay in the shadows and reap the profits silently. The boss did not always look out for the welfare of the miners and when the miners were neglected, this just gave the bosses another way to cover up more mistakes. It never hurt to have important people on one's side. All that interested the boss was getting the coal out of the mine and making a large profit, not caring about the possible death or injury of the miners, whether the danger was to humans or animals. This was true at Shantytown or any other mine throughout the history of coal mining.

Everyone in Shantytown used the doctor's house and office to gain relief from pain or ailment, as it was the only medical facility around. Many times the doctor's office and his home served as a hospital and dental facility. The doctor's knowledge was minimal, and tools were still very crude during this period of time. There were many brutal amputations and many lives lost.

The only known cure for a toothache was extraction. This was a painful process and without x-rays to examine, the wrong tooth was often pulled. Reliable anesthesia, preventive medicine, and x-rays, all of which were needed for setting broken bones, pulling teeth and amputating limbs, would have to wait for their discovery in the future.

When the drug called Morphine was available and used to lessen the pain, the doctor had to be careful the patient did not become addicted. Many of the doctors did not know how to administer the new medicines available to them, and often overdoses were the results of trial and error. The drug called ether was highly flammable and also required a great deal of experience to administer properly. One or two too many drops of this powerful anesthetic and the patient might not wake up on time, or at all. Both of these drugs were unobtainable because of cost. There was heavy demand for drugs of pain relief and use as an anesthetic, especially for the richer and larger hospitals just getting started in the bigger cities. Opium was another drug being brought in through overseas trade. Even though this drug had been in existence for centuries, it was still fairly new to medicine and its capabilities had not been thoroughly explored for medical use. Opium was also very expensive, and its availability was largely limited to the larger cities and waterway trading centers.

CHAPTER TWO
JOHN WORKS IN THE MINES

John was the third of seven children and with two older brothers, Todd and Andrew, already working in the anthracite mine; he was destined to take his turn. His younger sisters and brothers, too young for the mines were still required to take their turns helping the family through many hardships, as they paid the company store for everything they used. Many miners did not realize how many supplies they had bought on credit until they looked at the cost, which continued to mount on the ledger. Many times the items charged were questionable, but the miners were told they signed for the item, so they must have received it.

One of John's first jobs in the mine, while he was learning to become a miner was to tend the mules and their carts. John was only seven years old when he started, and a twelve-hour shift is a long time for an adult, much more so for a child. Many of the children in Shantytown started as young as six years old. Two of the many jobs handled by the younger children, were mule attendant and door operator. Just because these jobs were being done by young children did not mean they were easier, safer, or that they required shorter shifts.

Usually after working the breakers and picking out the slate from the coal for a couple of years, the young boys would look forward to becoming door-boys in the mines later, mule-boys, and then, laborers and helpers. Finally, when they were grown, they could become real miners, provided life allowed them to get that far or a disease of some kind had not made it impossible to continue working. There were always some exceptions, as in John's case. John worked the mines and never had to work the breaker. This was because some strings were pulled by his father, already an experienced miner, and extremely well liked by the foremen. Sean knew his way around with explosives and was considered an expert. Sometimes the miner's younger sons were allowed to do jobs usually done by older children, but these were the chosen few. This meant some of the accepted rules were changed, increasing the profits for the owner and the miner's family. The youngsters could be used at any age, for any job, as long as they did the job that was required of them. Since there were no labor laws there was little concern for the ages of the children or where they worked.

As for the mules, their life span was not very long underground, seldom exceeding seven years, while their normal life expectancy above ground exceeded twenty years. Never to view daylight again, many of the reliable and surefooted animals became blind within a short time after being taken underground. After the mules became blind, they only responded to pulling the heavy coal cars and worked by being led with a rope. Mule tending was one of the many jobs attended to by the young boys working in the mines. Many times the blind mule's reactions were from responding to repetitious work, and not from actually seeing where they were going. If a mule were allowed to return to the surface, exposed once more to the sunshine, after the utter darkness they had endured, it was sure they would not return below the surface again. The splendor of the sky, the breezes, the trees and grass would break upon them suddenly causing them to be filled with a mulish glee. Usually no cajoling could induce the mules to return to the depths of the mine.

The boys were often caught or pinned between the car and wall when they tried to stop the coal cars with a pointed wooden spike. The spike was stuck between the iron spokes of the wheels and would stop the wheel from turning. This would cause the wheel to drag or slide on the track until the car slowed down and stopped. These boys were always being hurried to get another car of coal to the surface, or forced to respond rapidly to the signal to send a string of empty cars down the rails, into the mine. A string of steel cars, even unloaded could not be easily stopped. Trying to stop a freewheeling car, especially if one lost one's balance or if the mineshaft at that point was to narrow between the car and the sides of the shaft to bend down without being run over, was quite an accomplishment in itself. These were only some of the hazards that caused the young boys the loss of their arms, legs or sometimes their lives. All that kept the mules from being run over and possibly dragged under the cars, crushing and killing them was the boys slowing the cars down with the wooden spike in the spokes. They had no other way to stop a runaway car, as there were no brakes on the cars or on the wheels. There was no way the mules could have held back that much weight at one time, once the momentum began. The young boys jobs of attending the mules, opening and closing of the main shaft doors and attending the cars, even though they did not always receive the deserved credit, was indeed very important in the lives of everyone working in the mine.

If a runaway car hit the big wooden door in the main shaft, it usually meant death to the victim caught inside, especially if he was not paying strict attention to the sound on the rails that warned of an approaching car. There was only standing room between the coal cars and the sides of the shaft, one of the main reasons small boys did this job. The boys were allowed to have a small wooden stool, so they could sit down and wait for the next car, if there was a delay.

One of the main delays was the shoring up of timbers overhead and on the sides of the tunnel to prevent a cave in. This was always a necessity and it was a time consuming task. These delays caused a mandatory closure of the tunnel and gave the boys some rest. But even though the delays were mandatory, the mine owners did not happily accept them. They expected a full days work for a full day's pay. The pay was determined by how many carloads of unprocessed coal, weighed by the ton, could be gotten out of the mine. Only then was it determined what amount of money the miner received for his day's wages. This salary was not paid on an hourly wage system. If there was no coal removed from the mine, then the miners weren't paid. Wasted productivity time showed no profit for the owner and the miners were not paid. There was a time schedule put out as to how many cars the boss expected to be moved through the door system in a given amount of time. If this schedule was not met, the boss had grounds for the dismissal of the boys from these jobs. This was done without explanation, as there were no unions and no set rules for the miners, their helpers or the other workers in the mine.

Never was safety mentioned as a responsibility of the owner. If someone got hurt, it was due to his own carelessness and nothing to rectify the situation was going to be done by the mine owner. There was a problem staying awake so the main shaft doors could be opened and shut for each passing car. The boy inside the two sets of doors did not receive a warning when the cars were coming through, and did not always have time to stand up and get beside the door. The car passed through to the next set of doors before going on its way to the place where the coal was lifted to the outside. There was not enough room for John to sit and have the car pass without his getting run over or crushed against the wall. The cold, darkness and dampness down in the mine often made him sleepy. For a young child working that long without rest, if he sat down very long, sleep was sure to come. All John was given to light his way was a small kerosene lamp on the brim of his hat that was attached with a band. In some cases the boys had only a small candle, in a small tin cup. The kerosene for the lamp cost more than the candle, not to mention the cost of the lamp. Neither of these devices gave much light and did not project the light very far ahead for him to see if obstacles were in his path of departure to other sections of the shaft. Having two small children work the door together to keep each other awake was not permitted because the mine owner claimed they would play and not pay attention to their job. Obviously, it was too costly to pay them both for the same job that one could do just as easily.

The two sets of doors that needed to be opened worked in conjunction with one another. When one set was opened, the other set was kept closed. This was a requirement, so there was not a wind tunnel effect created throughout the mine. Opening the first door coming from the mine and getting the mule and car inside and closing the heavy wooden door was only part of the job. John had to get past the coal car and get around front, so the remaining door could be opened for the car to continue, and then closed before the next car entered. John could not linger, as there was always another car and mule with driver waiting to come through.

Without the double door protection, there would be a constant flow of air streaming into the mine entrance, making it much colder, with a draft coming straight through to the airshaft that led outside to the top of the ground. The doors worked as a temperature control for the shafts. Later heat was introduced and used in the mines the same way oxygen was sent throughout the mine, with a fan and door system, but that is another story and did not happen here.

If there were a cave-in the proper equipment to dig out from the inside was frequently not available or was lost in the cave-in and hopelessly trapped beneath the timbers, coal and rock. Whether a miner could dig his way out, depended on how deep he was and how many feet of earth would have to be moved, without a supply of fresh flowing air. In most cases digging out toward the top was an impossible task, but to dig and hit another tunnel along side of the tunnel that caved-in was often tried and usually very successful without causing another cave-in. Sometimes, depending on what had happened and how bad the accident was, only one or two shafts of the mine had to be evacuated and then only to another shaft. Once they were either above or below the problem area, they could render assistance in digging from the other end to clear and repair the damaged area quicker, as their productivity time counted.

The airshaft to the top of the ground was not only a way for air to get into and out of the mine, but could also be used as a rescue tunnel for trapped miners. When a cave-in happened in the main tunnel to the outside, how was one to get out? Being manually pulled up the airshaft was often their only means of survival and escape.

When the airshaft was used for survival purposes and there was no other way to retrieve the miners, a rope was dropped to the bottom of the shaft, or to the required level where the miners were trapped. This operation was accomplished by using a makeshift winch, which was erected over the air duct allowing the victims to be removed, one at a time, from the mine.

A miner was securely strapped into a makeshift harness. The harness reached entirely around his shoulders and chest, so the air was not squeezed out of him. He stepped into a slot that was previously cut in the airshaft for rescue and attached the rope to the harness. The miner was lifted to safety with the help of a mule or men on top of the ground, pulling the rope and winding up the winch. Sometimes if a winch was not present, rope and pulleys were erected on a strong beam supported by timbers for legs over the air duct. This was only done as a last resort and rarely practiced.

To step into the shaft was fine when one was on the ground floor, but a different approach was required when on a higher level. There were no platforms to stand on in the shaft, as that would block the airflow in the duct. Pieces of metal were attached to the inside of the duct for the miner to step onto, not giving much support while standing straddled across the shaft. The inside of the air duct was always wet, slimy and slippery from the condensation, mineral deposits and water in the shaft. Many times the person being rescued was hurt worse from slipping off of the metal strips before securely hooking the lifting harness, and falling down through the air tunnel, than if he had waited for help to respond to the original accident. This was an accepted ordeal, as there were no safety precautions in place to be followed.

In all the time John worked in the mine, he could recall using this way out just once. There had been a cave-in on one of the upper levels and the mine entrance was to be closed for five days because of the heavy rock that fell from just beneath the earth's surface. They had to evacuate because of foul air in the tunnels and the lack of fresh oxygen for them to breathe. This was a very time consuming cost to the owner.

One method used as an early warning device for foul air, better known as methane gas, which was carried by the miners into the shafts, was a canary in a small wire cage. These pockets of gas or foul air that lacked oxygen and were unfit for survival in the earth were often uncovered while digging for coal. This gas could, and often did, catch fire and explode causing cave-ins and death. When this method was used, it required that a watchful eye be kept on the canary. This might be the miner's only warning when the bird fell off of its perch, to its death. If the dead canary was not seen too late, the miners evacuated the tunnel before an explosion from gas or a possible cave-in happened in the mineshaft. A premature or a delayed dynamite blast was not the only cause of cave-ins. When a pocket of gas was uncovered and ignited, sometimes by no more than a spark from a miner's pick death or injury to anyone in the vicinity of the blast occurred. The reaction from the explosion caused cave-ins throughout the shafts, which led to further injury and death, not only for the miners and their crews, but also for the mules as well. Cave-ins were brutal and cruel-crushing, mutilating and destroying anything in their path.

When John got older he and many of the other workers brought an extra sandwich to keep the rats around for their comfort and as an early warning device. The miners trusted and accepted the rats as their friends. They wanted them close at hand, so they could be watched for any unusual behavior. No one in the mine would allow harm to come to the rats. When John saw the rats leaving an area in the mine, he knew it meant trouble ahead. The rats always had their extremely keen senses turned on for survival and they could easily recognize danger, many times feeling the tremors of the earth long before the miners could. The rats would flee the area long before an incident occurred. This always gave the miners plenty of time for escape, provided they paid attention to and watched the rats.

Another important safety device was the drainage and pumping system. It was very important to keep it in operating order or the shafts below the surface would flood, killing everything below the surface. The mighty fans in the airshafts were required to work endlessly, moving the air from shaft to shaft and tunnel to tunnel. The fans had to work or the miners would suffocate and die from the lack of oxygen in the foul air. The explosions of dynamite and black powder did not help matters especially with the flying debris and smoke that was always present throughout the mine. Too many rules and regulations would put a burden on production, stopping the flow of coal. Numerous people needing work were always there as replacements, waiting to be employed, ready to work underground, without questions about rules. No child labor laws or general safety laws were put into place until much later.

CHAPTER THREE
LIFE IN SHANTYTOWN

The foremen of the shifts were usually friends or relatives of the boss. Their job was to oversee the miners and keep the shifts going night and day, using a rotational twelve-hour shift.

The foremen's homes, usually a little smaller in size, were well furnished, but the homes for the miners included only the bare necessities and had no luxury equipment in their two-room enclosures. A coal burning cook stove, a makeshift bed, and four chairs and table, were all a miner's family could expect. Sometimes a dresser was left by a previous owner. This was not much space for a family of nine, definitely requiring an extra room or two that would be added at the miner's expense, with lumber and nails to be purchased at the company store. The miner, not having any money, would sign the ledger for his purchases, a way of keeping the miner in debt to the company store. No doubt this is where the phrase of, "I owe my soul to the company store," originated.

The owners of the mine usually owned the company store and charged outrageous prices.

The experienced bookkeeper, whom the mining companies hired to do their bookwork, outmatched the wits of the uneducated miner. Oddly, the mistakes found were always to the benefit of the owners of the mines and never to the miners. Many times items were charged to the miners that someone else had or had not received, sometimes done intentionally. If a miner could not read he signed the ledger and really didn't know if he had signed for the correct quantity, only taking the bookkeeper's word. Many times the kerosene bought in the company store was watered down until what came out of the kerosene lamp was mostly smoke. Miners were required to purchase their powder or dynamite, fuse and caps from the same store that was charging them many times the initial cost. Often the miner could not get the proper strength dynamite that was required and often substituted with black powder and dynamite mixed in the same hole. This caused delays in the powder going off and one really was not always sure of the outcome of the blast. Supplies that were obtained from elsewhere or those not purchased in the company store could not be used in the mine and were labeled as a safety hazard, preventing their usage.

It was a miner's responsibility to pay his

John's family lived on the right side of this duplex.

help, even though all he received was seven cents per ton for the unprocessed coal his helpers shoveled and loaded on the cars. Any cost from the store became his responsibility as a number one priority before he or his help got paid. Many miners would draw a blank, meaning that, what he owed to the company store, came out first and there was nothing left for him or his family's needs. When his help received a blank from him, they usually quit. They did not owe the store and obviously they could not afford to work without wages. This kept the miner in constant debt to the store and required him to work harder, getting the coal out of the ground with less help.

Usually one day a month, provided some money was available, John's mother Dolly and some of the other miner's wives would walk five and a half miles, to the local town. They would buy essentials and necessities that were unobtainable from the company store or just cheaper. They could not buy great quantities, buying only what they could carry the long distance. Sometimes, Dolly would keep out three cents to buy some brown sugar and make a sweet string chew. This sweet chew was something the children always looked forward to, but learned not to expect. To make the chew, these items were required: a piece of cord string; some water; a pan and some brown sugar. Making a paste of the sugar that would stick to the string required very little boiling water. The cord string was cut into various lengths, depending on how big a chew she wanted to make; then soaked in the mixture and dried in the sun until it became hard. The children chewed or sucked on the string until it became soft and the sweetness was gone. John, even as an adult, remembered chewing the string before discarding it and remembered how the sweetness lasted after the sugar melted off the string. Oh, memories, sometimes, are trying to the soul.

There was a school in town, but the miners' children rarely attended it or at best irregularly. The long walk and the children having to work long hours were the main reasons. Occasionally one might hear of a child finishing fourth grade, but that was extremely rare. The mothers taught their children, and then, only so the child could sign his name, usually just enough to sign the ledger at the company store. Most of the boys were employed in the mines and had no time for book learning. After a day in the mine, sleep was required to prepare one's body for the next day when the same routine would be repeated.

Books and learning were usually available for the girls, when they were not doing their chores or working in the textile and silk factories, provided a factory was close enough for them to walk to work. This is assuming the lady of the house was educated and capable of teaching others what she, herself, had been taught. If books were not available, slate tablets and chalk were used. This was a time when book learning was not legally required, even though it was an important issue to the miner. Had the miner known that education could have helped him at the company store, he might have paid more attention and changed his life. Survival was the top priority and too much book learning would make the miners smarter than the mine owners. Then there would be no one to work the mines.

These people were slaves regardless of their color or creed; the mine owners and bosses did not respect the human life of a miner or the workers. If a man died in the mine, there was always someone else to take his place. If his family was lucky enough to have someone else to work, then they could remain in the shanty they called home. If no one was available to work, they were moved out and that was that, no remorse on anyone's part. The mine owners did not burden themselves with the family's welfare after none of them were left to work. The owner's only thought was getting the coal out of the ground and making money, not the plight of poor immigrant slaves. The miners worked two twelve hour shifts and if the men in the house were on two different shifts, which was usually the case, the women were required to have two different breakfast and supper times. Each man or boy carried his own tin bucket and canteen. Each tin bucket had to be packed with lunch, which was always cold by lunchtime.

Clothing maintenance was a required chore as clothes for the children and miners were a daily necessity. Clothing was constantly getting torn or just rotten from the lye used in the soap. The constant moisture in the mines was also detrimental to the clothes. The miner often had to go through water from the time he left the miners' car all the way to where his digging began. The mighty pumps above and below the ground helped to keep the water to ankle height, making walking through the main shaft easier. He would spend many long hours lying, crawling and digging in the dampness and underground seepage of water before actually getting the coal loaded into the cars. Some of this time was used to set the

As the family grew, Sean added rooms to the back of the house.

powder charges that had to be tapped into solid rock, a slow process whereby a star drill and a sledgehammer were used for drilling the holes.

The miners were never rich enough to have the luxury of very many extra clothes, and there were no local clothing stores. Their clothes were always made and repaired right at home. John was lucky to have sisters, in addition to his mother, for mending and making clothes. The clothes were cut out of a large piece of material. After pinning the pattern to the material and cutting around the pattern as a guide, the pieces were sewn together. The whole family often shared in the making of their clothes; each member could do their part, and this was a way to teach the youngsters to sew. When John tried cutting with the scissors, which were small for his big hands, he quickly found it was not easy to follow a straight line. He decided he would not try the pattern method, as material was hard to come by and he did not really have the time required to make clothes. He did find out sewing with a needle and thread was not difficult once the needle was threaded. In that day and time one had to learn how to survive and sewing, as well as cooking and many other essential skills were important to know.

In the family everyone had his or her own special job, but that did not mean they did not know how to do each other's jobs. This was a part of living and something everyone automatically practiced and understood. One added job, mainly for the women in their already busy day, was to make the soap, which they used in the daily cleaning and laundry routine. One of the main ingredients for making the soap was lye, which was obtained from water draining slowly through wood ashes into a wooden bucket. This required another unmentioned chore to be done, as the houses were only equipped with coal burners. A small fire would be started outside with wood and the coals and ashes were gathered, so the lye could be obtained. A wooden bucket or bowl was used to catch the lye because the lye was an acid that would eat through a metal container.

Laundry was another chore that was required during all four seasons, and even though it was a daily routine, it never became easy. The springs, wells and the water-holding tanks were intentionally located at the other end of Shantytown, or this was the way it always seemed. Sometimes, the miner thought, his house was located in the wrong place. Well this time, if the house were located on the other end of

Shantytown by the spring, at least the water would have been simpler and easier to get for the laundry. The carrying of water, usually by hand, a great distance, was a backbreaking ordeal. To have a washing tub of water to bathe in required carrying as many as four of the five-gallon buckets of water. These were usually brought by hand from the spring at the other end of town. This was a great distance, provided one even had the buckets to use for the water. Buckets, along with anything else that was needed, could be purchased at the company store and, as always, could be added to the ledger. Making many necessary trips back and forth until the tubs were filled or the clothes were washed was just a routine day in the miner town. When John was about four years old the mine owner started to supply a mule drawn wagon with barrels of water for the residents of the town to receive their buckets of water daily. The wagon helped but was mainly on a first come, first served basis. The barrels and the wagons held just so much, and when the barrels were emptied the drivers were through with the water detail and had other duties to attend to for the day.

When John didn't have a bunch of chores to do, he loved to ride the water wagon, as it gave him the feeling of moving around quickly. He liked the jiggling effect the wagon made in his stomach and he enjoyed the ride from one end of town to the other, without having to walk or run as he usually did. Running was something all children did, but it made John feel special. John just seemed to have energy to burn and never seemed to tire.

Bathing was quite a chore, because the water had to be heated on the coal stove and the miners had to pay for the coal they burned. Sometimes coal pieces would be found along the road or between the ties that were under the railroad rails leaving Shantytown. Even though the miners or their family were not stealing the coal, they still had to be careful or they would be accused of thievery. Legally the coal still did not belong to the miners even if it was found lying on the ground because the land belonged to the owner and anything on it.

In the winter there was always ice to contend with, and when the ponds were frozen getting water really became a chore. This often required everyone's help, regardless of age. Cutting the ice usually required help and the walkway was always slippery from the water being spilled. The miners would all chip in and cut ice to be stored in the icehouse. Since everyone in Shantytown used the ice it was only fair that everyone pitch in and help cut and store it. Every year the ice hole had to be leveled out and the sides reinforced again. After a few years of observing and helping, John was given the responsibility of filling the ice-hole. He had to help dig out or shore up the hole each year before winter froze the ground too hard for a pick, bar and shovel to easily be used. John said, "I never saw a pick, bar or shovel that is easy to use, but when one is used properly, work seems easier." A big hole was dug in the ground that was eight to twelve feet deep and ten feet wide for the ice to be stored. Once the ice was insulated properly, it would last well into the summer months. The proper way of preserving the ice was to put down a layer of sawdust, adding a layer of ice, layer of sawdust, etc. until the hole was filled, and then to put a thick layer of sawdust on top. When that much sawdust could not be obtained, straw was the next best insulation. Just using regular stove ashes also worked as insulation and was often used. The ice remained in the frozen state much longer, provided the ashes could be kept dry. The dryness caused the ashes to remain light and fluffy which insulated the ice from the air, keeping in the cold and keeping out the heat. The sawdust and straw were often combined as a mixture and worked very well in holding the temperature at freezing, preserving the ice. When it was possible, a roof of some design was erected, as it helped to keep the rain and the hot sun from beating down directly on the ice. A shallow ditch was dug around the ice-hole, so the rainwater coming off the roof could be carried away, without soaking in the ground. Extra water in ice-hole would cause the ice to melt quicker than normal. The ice was not a rationed item and anyone could use as much as they wanted, provided they helped to restore and replenish the ice in the hole next year. There was always ice left over at the end of summer. The only thing wrong with using the ice, in John's mind, was when the ice started getting low in the hole, it was a reminder to him that winter was not far away. John did not really mind the cold. He knew how to dress in layers for warmth, but this ice thing every year was really starting to bother him and he decided it was soon going to be someone else's turn. He really liked doing this job and the added responsibility and he really wasn't going to quit. John was just trying to get everyone interested in helping and getting the job done faster and more easily with everyone's assistance. It was his plan that everyone work together to accomplish the job.

Sunday was a day of rest for the miners and their families. This was a day set aside for them to thank their Lord in church. Even though it was Sunday, most of the daily chores were still required, as it was just another day of life. Most of the miners were immigrants, just like John's family, and had brought their own religious beliefs with them to this new land. There was, at that time in the miner's life, not much choice as to what church or denomination he or his family would attend. The mine owners did not recognize the immigrants' church or chosen religion and a building or a church was not established for them. Many of the miners and their family met among themselves or not at all. John's mother was a religious person and had strong beliefs about prayer. Many times her friends and neighbors would meet in front of her house on their way to church. The whole family would be there and together they would all join hands and pray before heading off to church. John's family by themselves made a big circle and with help from the others, as they joined in, the circle would extend out into the street.

Religion was important only to the immigrants. Many of the mine owners only used religion to keep the miners happy. If the owners of the mine could have gotten more coal without giving a break in the week, it would have been done. This day of rest was also an important issue to the miner. It allowed a break for him before he followed the same routine for another week.

Yes, the miners and their families had a harsh life and the days of mining for coal, better known as black gold, would take many lives. Many times the wives or children would go outside to find their loved one's remains left on the porch without even a knock on the door. Death had passed by, leaving its mark. Accidents happened often, frequently causing death, not a pretty picture of the coal miners' way of life. Often their fellow workers of the human race treated each other as strangers when death was present. All of this was for a few pennies more, one person having control over the other, another type of slavery for a few more earthly possessions.

John had become restless over the past years and an unconscious discontent feeling was starting to act up. It was like a fever he could not break. Neither rest nor medicine could end this feeling that was overtaking him. In his childhood years this feeling appeared like a ghost out of nowhere and made him want to ramble, always in motion and never being still. People would say, "He certainly is a rambunctious child," or "He's bursting out with loads of energy and always on the go." They did not know this constant urge to move around would stick with John for life, becoming much stronger as he grew older. Sometimes, this feeling would last longer than a few miles out of town or a short outing in the forest. He would get the urge to roam around with no particular place to go. It would be awhile before he would understand why he had a feeling that something was drawing him away from this life as a miner.

CHAPTER FOUR
RAMBLING FEVER

John was a young man of nineteen years when he decided to do some traveling. He had a dream and saw a different way of life for himself. Being poor and in a hole in the ground was not going to be his way of life any longer. With the beginning of the year well into spring and after losing two brothers, a sister and his father in mine tragedies over the past few years, John had to do something. He knew there was something out there, something that could change his life and the lives of his family forever. He was tired of being poor and being told where to dig and when to be there. All of this was just too much to bear for this individual. He could escape a fate of being sent down a lonely shaft, maybe never to return, or to be buried alive.

One morning instead of going to work in the mine, he decided to quit the only way of life he knew and to find a different future. He decided to leave the family in Shantytown, as it was the only work they knew. He would send for them when he found work and a place to stay, sometime in the near future. John did not know what he was going to do, but anything would be better than this, for all he was doing was existing.

Without really having any plans for the future and with very little money saved, he wandered through the wilderness seeing an occasional log cabin or a little settlement along the trail. He would stop for awhile and do some little job for a bite to eat, sometimes being offered a roof over his head for the night. Everyone he met was very friendly and he was never turned away hungry, often being offered food for the road. John was not sure what he was looking for but he was determined to find it, hoping that whatever it was he would find soon. When he was wondering what would he see over the next hill, there it was in front of him, more water than he had ever seen or dreamed possible to be in one place. This was surely a miraculous sight: water so blue in color and white sands under his feet, water as far as the eye could see and beyond. He had reached the Atlantic Ocean. It was as if another world was calling to him, to come and join the water and so he did-he became a fisherman. He caught more fish and bigger fish than anyone would believe. He had little difficulty making friends with the people in the little coastal town. His new friends told him the names of many of the species of fish. People passing by would say that's a nice Stripper, Flounder, Ring Perch, Spot, Barracuda, Blue Fish or what-ever kind of fish it was that he had caught. These names were useless to him as there were thousands of fish and so many names he could not remember them all; so he called this one blue, this one brown, that one yellow. There were so many different kinds it was hard to count that high, much less keep track of how many kinds he had already seen and caught. He would not keep more of the fish than were needed for food, but he loved the excitement of catching them and then he would release them. From before the sun rose in the morning until long after dark John could be found fishing along the shore.

While visiting Boston, one of the larger and more colorful coastal towns along the ocean, John heard many tales that were being spread by the sailors. They told of other lands and countries. Some of the stories were true, while many of them were only for the sailors' pleasure, so they could watch John as he stared in amazement. The different dress and culture of each country were amazing to John. He was really not much for socializing, but he had to hear more about the curious lands and the amazing tales, whether they were true or false. The sailors told of fish as big as ships, weighing many tons, which, John found out later, were whales. They even told John that there were other oceans besides this one and some even bigger. John was not too sure about becoming a sailor and decided to wait a while, because his land loving legs were just not ready to give way to the ocean as yet. He would have to make a decision on that subject at a later date.

One particular story that intrigued him was about pure golden statues and how people were always fighting for the gold and carrying it from city to city. It was as though the one with the most gold was the winner. Gold interested John. He liked hearing about how easy it was to obtain. Many stories were told and some told of pirates who sailed and ruled the seas. The pirates would capture the crews of other ships and sell them as slaves to other pirate ships or dealers in slave trade. Some of the stories were quite colorful; others told of sadness and sorrow. John decided not to be a pirate as he already suffered enough sadness. John did give some thought to obtaining one of those golden statues. How different things would be for him and his family if he could find a little gold.

John tried making a boat and sailing around for awhile, never leaving the sight of land. Actually, he accomplished the task quite easily, making a very sturdy and reliable seaworthy boat. To a foreigner it might have looked like a raft that was tied together with grapevines for binding, with a pole sticking out of the middle. John, being the sailor he was, after attaching the mast and sail, decided it resembled a boat. This living and acting like a sailor would not last. Yes, he was having fun, but it was not fulfilling, it just was not what he wanted to accomplish with his life and he had not forgotten his family. Time was not waiting any longer, as little over a year had passed very quickly. A calling from the distance was beckoning him to follow. John found himself leaving Boston and the Coast, retracing his footsteps, and returning home to the little miners' village.

He knew this stay was not going to be very long, but he needed to share his experiences and new findings with his family. His family was very excited to see him, as they had not heard from him and didn't know if he was still alive. He told them many tales about his experiences and his excellent sailing around the ocean in his boat. He intentionally forgot to explain how he had never left the sight of land. His real reason was not necessarily because he may have gotten lost or because his boat was not big enough to sustain the mighty waves, but he did not want them to know he didn't know how to swim. Swimming was something that he had never learned as a child growing up in Shantytown, and definitely did not come naturally to him. There were several times when he thought he would drink the ocean dry. Finally, he would reach shallow enough water for him to stand on the sand with his head out of the water, making breathing again possible. John quickly found his limits and learned to do a good dog paddle.

CHAPTER FIVE
THE IRON HORSE

What was about to happen to John he had never before experienced. Gold fever was about to take over his soul and he would venture into another toughening experience. This would become a routine for him later in life, but it was just the beginning of a long era, that would definitely change his life forever. This time he had decided to go west and make a living looking for gold. When he found gold, he might even make himself one of those statues the sailors told him about that were so plentiful in the orient. On his way west he intended to find time to trap some of the many fine pelts the Easterners were wearing and make his fortune quickly. He planned to return home by early spring and start a new life in Boston or one of the big cities on the coast, also moving his family to a life of luxury.

John's mother remained in Shantytown with his sister and brothers for a while longer. Mining was still the only way of life they knew. John had always had a fever to travel, and this time he had a few dollars saved for the journey. Besides, how long would it take to pick up enough gold to be happy for the rest of his life? This was to be an undertaking, which would require more knowledge and skills than he now possessed.

Eleven months out in the wilderness having found little or no gold had an effect on this man, who knew very little about where to look for gold. Gold might be here for the picking but John was picking in the wrong place. John needed to learn all he could about this yellow mineral and, lucky for him, he was willing and strong enough to work at odd jobs along the way. This gold fever was not an easy thing to get the hang of, or to explain. One either found gold or not. In searching for gold, there was no happy medium. There was food in the belly, money in the pocket or there wasn't. There definitely was no money to send home. Even if he had a way to send the money, there was none left to send.

Had it not been for his willpower and strength, his existence would have been short lived. While riding the railroad he could pick up a few extra dollars cleaning out railcars or cutting logs and splitting them for firing the boiler. The boiler heated the water and made the steam, and the steam, converted it to power, making the big iron engine move swiftly along the track. Sometimes the mighty engines would pull at least a mile of cars behind them to their destination. The Plains Indians called the steam engine, "The Iron Horse," and they feared the black smoke coming out of its smokestack, its harsh loud whistle, and the hot white "clouds" coming out of its sides. Sometimes the steam was so hot and under so much pressure that it was clear. If one of the Indians got in the way of a relief valve and the engine built up enough pressure to let off steam, it would cut the Indian just as if someone had used a knife on him. However the wound would not bleed because the steam would cauterize the wound. The Indians, who were already afraid of the train, now thought they had been cut by a demon with a special knife only used by an unseen force. Oh! The stories continued for many years throughout many Indian camps and it took years for the trains to be accepted by them. Many believed it was a living god of some kind that they had not been warned about, or it was one of their ancestors who had been wronged and was returning to destroy them. Their superstitions were real to them and, not understanding how the engine worked or having anyone to explain how it worked, they came up with the only explanation that made sense to them. Many people have kept these same superstitions alive in different forms; it is a shame when someone does not ask for an explanation and remains in the dark about simple things. Some of the flatbed cars were loaded with the steel rails and wooden railroad ties for the construction of new tracks, bringing civilization to this part of the New World. Sometimes coal was used for firing the boilers, but this was a tremendous cost to the railroad and not as efficient as wood. Trees usually grew close by the tracks and their wood could easily be obtained with an ax, crosscut saw, a little willpower and the railroad paying for labor for cutting, gathering and splitting the wood. For a little extra money or sometimes a free ride, John would agree to oil the train. There were a great number of places to oil that he did not know existed until he took the job. John had to crawl under the cars and grease the axles or climb on top and grease the heavy hinges and rollers inside the steel track on the boxcar doors. The train was not always stationary when the oiling was done. Anyplace there was iron, grease and oil was required to keep it from rusting. This was a job that John didn't care much for, but it generally allowed a free ride and free meals. Eating had become one of his favorite hobbies and he loved to eat regularly.

CHAPTER SIX
PACE MOUNTAIN

John was now a young man of 24 years with broad shoulders, a full black beard and coal black hair flowing down past his shoulder blades. He had been gone from the mining village for five years, except for the last short visit, which he still remembered well. He was definitely on his way to becoming a mountain man and he was being primed for the role. Destiny was riding silently by his side and waiting for the proper moment to appear. John drifted from one frontier town to the next, not staying long anywhere, just picking up a few dollars and moving on to where fate and the rails would carry him. He wired most of the money from his small amount of gold findings and odd jobs to his family, helping them out whenever he could, often wishing he could do more.

Many times a little gold could be panned, another type of mining, where water in a sluice box, or just a metal pan, and a stream of water was used to find gold. Often, there was nothing left to send home because even bumming around across the territory and trying to find his fortune in gold cost a considerable amount of money. A simple shovel became very expensive when gold was mentioned in the same sentence. The majority of the time, a pack animal and a grubstake cost many times more than John received in the return of gold. Traveling by train created an additional cost for the caring and hauling of the pack animal. John did not get a free ride either, even though he got to know most of the conductors in the cars and the engineers who ran the trains. What seemed an eternity of riding trains and packing out through the wilderness while searching for gold was becoming a way of life for John and one he did not care for.

On what he thought was to be his last excursion, he rode a brand new steam engine into the little town of Pace Mountain, just one hundred and fifty miles south of Saint Louis, Missouri. Yes, progress and civilization were quickly moving westward. Some of the tales about the gold promised that it just lay on the ground for the taking. Though the stories were too good to be true, everyone young and old was speaking about the Promised Land and striking it rich. Pace Mountain was to be John's new home for a while. He needed a grubstake, a good rifle and some transportation before going to the gold fields and really striking it rich. While riding on the last train before coming to Pace Mountain, John sold most of his mining possessions to a new prospector, making it possible to afford this trip, still hoping to fulfill his desire to strike it rich.

CHAPTER SEVEN
THE BLACKSMITH

John was easily liked by everyone who made contact with him. He always quickly learned any task; especially those encountered while being employed at the local livery stable. Mr. Kolar was the owner and the only blacksmith for many days' ride. John learned many things that would help him later through tough times while being employed by Mr. Kolar.

John knew nothing of shoeing horses or making horseshoes, but having a good teacher, along with trial and error, helped him to become a very skilled blacksmith. Making new harnesses and repairing old or worn out pieces of leatherwork gave John another trade to learn. The things he learned to restore or make from scratch were numerous. Many tricks of the trade were also learned, and the jobs became easier when short cuts were taken. John was the first person in the town to design and make his own leather bed. The pattern for the bed was sold in the local leather store and some were put in the general store as well. He was given a small percentage for every pattern sold by the storekeepers.

Making buggy wheels with steel rims was also very easy for him, once he got the hang of welding the ends together so they did not come apart. John became a carpenter's apprentice with the little time he had to spare. Besides, he was already skilled with the tools required to shore and brace up the mine tunnels back in Pennsylvania. What he learned in the mines would reward, as well as haunt, him throughout his life. Knowing more of the carpenter's ways would be a tremendous help. Having this extra knowledge allowed him to fix and repair, gaining him many odd jobs throughout the town. On one occasion he even attempted to make some cabinets for the doctor's office, which turned out rather well. He just did not have the time to accommodate everyone's needs. Everyone wanted something done; they all wanted more done than he had the time to do, especially with all of the requirements from his other odd jobs. Really, it was Mr. Kolar who deserved his help, as he was the first person John worked for when he came to town. Now John was working part time all over town and really didn't have a full time job anywhere, becoming a jack-of-all-trades. He decided to slow down and mainly work for Mr. Kolar, taking on only an occasional part time job, but nothing regular as he had been doing. He really was glad to get the chance to relax a little and enjoy his surroundings, without becoming part of them, as he had been doing since his arrival in town.

As winter was fast approaching, a fur trader and trapper stopped by the livery stable with two mares, both in foal, and both for sale. The trader needed to move on quickly before the pass was frozen shut for the winter months, making travel impossible. He did not have time to stay in town and wait for the mares to foal, nor was he going to take the time for the young to become strong enough to endure the long tedious journey back home. Mr. Kolar, the livery stable owner, bought both mares for a decent price and made it sound like he was doing the trapper a favor. Really, Mr. Kolar was only in the Livery Stable business for the money and he saw a good chance to make a few extra dollars. Come spring, he would have four horses to sell for the price of two pregnant mares. He told the trader that they might not live giving birth or both the colt and the mother might die. He made it sound as though he might get the bad end of the bargain, and the trader, being in a hurry, took the deal. John was learning another lesson in life and all it required was to listen.

John was to keep an eye on the animals in case any emergency problems arose when the young were born, another added responsibility. He didn't mind and really wasn't seeing this as an added responsibility, as he had always loved animals and never wanted to see them hurt or in pain. He would always do anything he could to help, regardless of the time spent or the cost. One night, as a storm hit with winter exploding and thunder so loud he could not hear himself think, both colts were born without any trouble. Before the storm had completely passed and with the thunder still rumbling in the distance, both mares and colts were up and doing fine.

For a bonus and with Christmas fast approaching, Mr. Kolar gave John his pick of either colt for a job well done. John, who was just learning about horseflesh made a good pick, and chose the strawberry roan. As a perfect name to remember the occasion, he called him Thunder.

After many months of planning, John was now ready to move on and continue his search for gold. He had only one more stop before continuing on to the gold fields and that would be to one of the largest cities in the west, Saint Louis, Missouri.

CHAPTER EIGHT
JOHN'S RIFLE, TICKLER

John went to Saint Louis to obtain the already famous Hawken rifle and to request it to be made in a fifty-four-caliber with a full stock and double set triggers that worked correctly whether set or unset. Double set triggers meant that when the rear trigger was set or pulled, the front trigger only required a light touch of pressure to set off the rifle. This function is normally used when a rest is available for long distant or precision shooting.

Making this rifle to John's specification required a considerable amount of time, as all of the work required in making the rifle had to be accomplished by hand. The metal parts required time to shape and many adjustments were made before the final angles and cuts were made for their intended purpose. More than a week's worth of effort and hard work was required for the lock to function as smooth as a clock and to be timed to perfection.

The stock of fancy curly maple wood for this marvelous rifle also required special attention. After the wood had been selected for making the stock, the tedious long hours of shaping began. Just channeling out the wood for the barrel to fit precisely was a chore within itself. This was accomplished with a drawknife, a few rasps of different sizes, a small hewing tool and some flat, round, and very sharp chisels of different shapes and sizes. Making the proper pitch and drop in the stock was also necessary for the rifle to fit against John's shoulder and face correctly. The length of the trigger from the butt of the rifle depended totally on the length of the shooter's arms and each individual required a different pitch. This was just one reason each rifle was handmade for a particular individual and obviously added time to the task. Of course, when the carving and rasping were completed, the staining and finishing process began. This was a skill that required patience, as the gunsmith was almost finished with the rifle and did not want to make a mistake at the end stage. When one rifle was designed for a particular person, it would have to be altered before another person could shoot it correctly and maintain accuracy. Altering the stock was an art and could not be done by everyone. Just because someone owned a firearm did not mean he could repair it. Many people adapt to a rifle built for someone else, rather than have it properly fixed by a gunsmith, because they don't know a correction is possible.

Making the barrel required long strips of red-hot steel to be wrapped and welded around a steel rod. The rod was close to the finished size of the caliber of the rifle an individual desired. The barrel was made by pounding the red-hot strips of steel with a heavy steel hammer on an anvil, around the steel rod inside, while mixing in with the wrapped steel, a dry form of flux mixture, causing a form of welding to take place. Once the welding process was completed and the steel rod was removed, the finished product was called Damascus twist steel barreling. This was a soft, giving steel, that would withstand a lot of inside pressure from being shot, without rupturing the barrel.

Some of the best knife blades also were made from Damascus steel. A Damascus steel blade required very little effort on a sharpening stone to obtain a scalpel edge. Also Damascus steel would hold this edge much longer than a regular steel blade. A knife blade required a different process to accomplish the finished product even though they were both called Damascus steel after being finished.

The type of ignition to be used for the rifle was discussed thoroughly between John and Mr. Hawken before a final decision could be made. There was a new type of firing mechanism to be considered, as many gunsmiths were replacing the flint ignition with the priming cap. The cap is a thin piece of metal that contains a detonator. When the cap is placed over the nipple that extends into the powder behind the ball and struck by the cock or hammer, it explodes on contact, causing fire to go through the nipple and ignite the powder behind the bullet. John did not know this type of detonator ignition and with careful thought he chose the flintlock ignition over the cap. He was also thinking about not having a store out in the wilderness to readily buy caps, an absolute requirement for the rifle to function properly. The flint type ignition for the flintlock rifle requires a piece of flint and a properly forged frizzen. The gunsmith used a heat tempering treatment on the iron that he used to make the frizzen. When a correctly tempered frizzen was hit with a piece of flint, the proper spark could be obtained to ignite the powder. The correct tightness of the flint, with a leather wrap, is held in place by the upper and lower jaw. The jaw screw regulates the tension on the flint and all of this is attached to the cock or hammer. When everything is correctly aligned, a spark will jump from the frizzen to the pan, igniting the fine powder, sending a flame through the touchhole and igniting the course powder. After ignition of the course powder the bullet is propelled out of the barrel and proceeds to the intended target. The rifle functions as required, having fire in the pan, belching a bullet, smoke from the barrel and recoil from the butt of the stock, all of which is required when shooting a flintlock rifle. This whole process of the flint ignition sounds complicated, but after the trigger is pulled, the actual firing happens instantaneously. The two different types of black powder were course and fine grain. When the commercial fine four-f powder required for the pan was not available, one could grind the course powder that was used for the actual propelling of the bullet. A touchhole (usually no more than five-sixty fourths of an inch in diameter) was drilled through the barrel from the inside of the pan. This allowed the flame to pass from the pan of fine granulated powder to the course powder behind the bullet. When two or more friends were parting on the trail or going their separate ways, one often heard, "Keep your powder dry". They were referring to the powder in the pan of the

Tickler

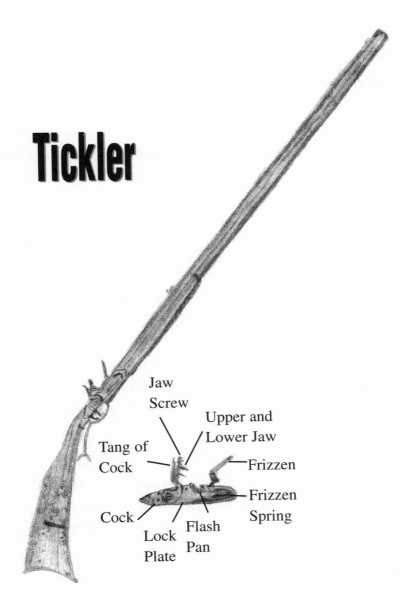

Jaw Screw

Upper and Lower Jaw

Tang of Cock

Frizzen

Cock

Frizzen Spring

Lock Plate

Flash Pan

Flintlock Rifle.

John found that the general rule practiced and accepted by the old timers was to use one to one and a half times the amount of powder, times the caliber of the rifle, for the required amount of powder behind the bullet for fifty caliber and above. When John was shooting a thirty-two-caliber rifle, the general rule did not apply. He would use approximately twenty-five grains of fine powder behind the bullet as the smaller diameter bullets went much faster and required yet another type of powder. It was found, through trial and error, when using the smaller caliber bullet, that to achieve the accuracy John desired, he had to decrease the amount of powder, usually by five or more grains.

When a loud high pitch report or a cracking sound of the rifle was achieved the weapon was ready for action. Too much powder would cause a lower booming noise and poor accuracy. The appropriate load for safety, maximum power, and accuracy of this particular fifty-four caliber Flintlock Rifle was eighty-one grains of coarse black powder behind a four hundred and fifty five-grain conical lead bullet. The conical bullet design of five hundred and thirty five thousandths diameter offered an improved terminal ballistics to flatten out more than the round patched ball upon impact, causing a larger exit wound and quicker death to the intended game or victim. This load gave considerably more recoil, also known as a kick, than the two hundred and thirty-grain round ball bullet, which required a patch before loading the ball on top of the powder. John made sure he had a mold for making the lead round ball bullet and another for the conical bullet before he left town.

The method of grinding black powder to priming powder was used only when the fine four-f powder could not be obtained from the store. The main tools required for this chore of grinding coarse powder to fine powder, were a hard surface that would cause no sparks, and two large wooden spoons. John sprinkled some course black gunpowder into one spoon and used the other to grind it until it was fine enough to meet his requirement.

The pan of the flintlock rifle required that this fine granulation of four-f powder, be filled no higher than just under the touchhole that was drilled through the pan and into the barrel. When four-f powder, as it was called, was obtainable, it was preferred to the home-ground method as it gave a faster burn. John test-fired the rifle or pistol with the load he intended to use, whether hunting or for sport. He was always careful and safe, making sure to have a good backstop for the lead bullets!

When John set up camp, a campfire was easily started by pulling the trigger on the rifle, causing the flint to strike against the frizzen. This created a spark to ignite the tender, which was under the prepared kindling. Sometimes John put the tender in the pan and after lighting it moved the burning tender to the kindling. The tender was usually dry pine bark mixed with pine resin or fine fibers of dry rope, sometimes even grass. The main requirement for tender was that it was easy to ignite and safe enough to transfer to the kindling without burning oneself in the process. Later, after the fire was started and properly burning, larger logs were added. Making fire also required the pan to be emptied of powder, or the charge in the rifle would ignite causing an unexpected discharge of the weapon. To be on the safe side, John fired the weapon into soft earth for easy retrieval of the lead before attempting to make fire. This beautiful weapon was one of John's many requirements in helping to make life easier while living off the land.

When John didn't trap or buy his food at the local settlement store, he made the best of what was on hand, or he hunted. Many times he shot his breakfast, lunch and supper. The size of his prey would determine how many meals he could make from a well-placed shot. When the shot was not well placed, there was no food for his effort. There was also no reward when the powder did not ignite or only the powder in the pan ignited and did not set off the main charge. A well-known term, often used by flintlock users was, "fire in the pan," or "no fire in the pan", as the case might be. Sometimes John just plain missed his intended target. This was not a time to forget to load the powder or the bullet in the rifle. Flinching from the recoil was definitely out of the question. Later in life this magnificent rifle would decide John's fate and become one of his most trusted possessions throughout his life. He lovingly named it Tickler.

CHAPTER NINE
THUNDER

John was admiring the vast country he was about to enter while sitting on Thunder, his magnificent strawberry roan stallion. John spent several hours removing the burs and thorns from the cactus and weeds that had become matted and lodged in Thunder's fluffy, long, thick, white main and tail that blew freely in the fresh mountain air. John often recalled Mr. Kolar's remarks about how easy Thunder, had been to train for riding. What Mr. Kolar did not know was that John had spent many days leading Thunder, placing a bag of wheat on the horse's shoulders and back, before he set an empty saddle on the horse's back and attempted to cinch it down. Still John didn't ride until more wheat, resembling the weight of a rider, was carried in the empty saddle for a few more outings. Finally John put his foot in the stirrup for the first time. That first real mounting, from the ground to the stirrup and into the saddle, was well worth the effort and training. The two were meant to be together. Thunder accepted the weight of this man without question. He had learned to trust him from the first night of his birth. Many a good man had vanished into this hard and unforgiving land. John knew that one wrong move or stupid mistake could cause him to join those who had passed beyond the mountains that reach the sky. Having a good steed under him was an important issue in this untamed land and it gave him something to talk to, as they moved to new adventures. Being brought up with hardships back east, where the day started before sunrise and ended well after dark, had caused this pilgrim to become a huge man. Not only his body was strengthening, but also his mind was strengthening with knowledge far beyond anyone's imagination. Usually a miner's life down in the tunnels ended in darkness with no light at the end of the tunnel. But look at John now!

THUNDER

CHAPTER TEN
FOOD FOR WINTER

John loaded the packhorses with enough supplies to brave the wilderness for nine months, before the winter got too bad for man or beast to endure. He knew after nine months' time, he would be required to seek shelter and food for relief from those awful blizzards encountered in the winter. This would require planning and timing to have enough supplies on hand and shelter for himself and his horses through the winter months.

Preparing food for the harsh winters required much preparation and hard work. In most cases a smokehouse and a root cellar were required to keep the prepared food through the winter months. The root cellar was usually for vegetables and all foods that required being kept cold but not frozen. The area towards the back of the cellar did not freeze, as the earth maintained an average of fifty-five degrees Fahrenheit year round. Through trial and error with different foods, John found that chicken, pheasant, guinea, duck and goose eggs could be kept for longer periods of time when stored in the cool temperature obtained in the earth cellar. Guinea eggs would keep the longest amount of time, with or without the cool of the cellar. When a cooler temperature was required for longer periods of time, John put ashes over the items needing storage, usually in a frame or box, keeping the ashes off the product. It was not uncommon to use up to two feet of ashes, which worked as an insulation barrier, helping to keep the cool in and the heat out. Sometimes he used lime over the vegetables, especially potatoes. However, lime was not an insulator, but was used as a preservative to deter rot from forming in the vegetables.

When the side of a hill was present and fairly accessible, preferably close to the kitchen, there was a likely spot for the root cellar. Usually, all that was required for the cellar was a five foot high by seven foot deep opening, dug back into the hill, with a slight slant to the outside. This tilt was required to drain the water and condensation from the inside that dripped down through the earth and roots. If the water didn't have a place to run off, it would cause rot, damage and spoilage to the contents put in the cellar. Adding a make shift door kept out the varmints, and the root cellar was finished. A roof was not required as the earth and Mother Nature had already provided the sod as a natural run off.

There was much more work required besides planting, caring for, weeding and picking the fruits and vegetables. After digging the cellar and getting it prepared for the winter, the process of preserving the food began. John had to accomplish this before winter set in, as none of the vegetables grew in the snow. When dried vegetables were required, John processed them by drying them near the fire to prevent spoilage. Blanching was sometimes required to partially cook them and seal in the flavor before drying was started. In the summer this was very trying, especially when the heat exceeded human endurance. When a fire was not required, many hours were required to turn the vegetables over from one side to the other. Keeping out the birds and rodents was a chore, as they were also looking for, and storing food, for the winter. Baking, drying, or parching, was required with corn, before storing it for long periods of time. Mold was fast growing and spoilage set in quickly, if the corn remained green. Some of the vegetables that required drying were tomatoes, beans (navy and string), broccoli, okra, peas, and spinach, which was often ground into flakes, as it did not return to its moist and natural state after being dried. Fruit that was dried required much the same process, with the fruit being cut into thin pieces, so the slices would dry evenly and not leave moisture in part of the piece, causing it to spoil and rot. Apricots, apples, peaches, pears and grapes were just some of the fruits that were dried. Regular root vegetables that kept very well during the winter, usually with their green tops attached, were carrots, pumpkin, winter squash, zucchini, parsnips, turnips, tomatoes (still green hanging on the vines), onions, white potatoes, and sweet potatoes. Many more varieties of vegetables were grown and stored in different root cellars, depending on where John lived at the time.

The smokehouse obviously required more complicated planning and more hard labor to build. John needed a building with a roof, storage space for meat to hang, a fireplace built inside the structure for smoking the items, and a preparation area. These were the main requirements for meat to be stored without spoilage. The smokehouse not only held meat but anything that required smoking. When obtainable, oysters and fish could also be smoked and preserved in the smokehouse, keeping them edible for many months.

Sometimes salt fish was kept in the smokehouse along with salted meat. These did not require smoking, but the smoke had the advantage of turning away many critters and insects that would have devoured the food if these precautions were not enforced. The smokehouse also served as a barrier to weather and to varmints, two legged as well as four. People have been known to kill one another for getting caught in the meat house without permission. People did not take kindly to thievery; John worked very hard for his food and sometimes it meant life or death to him. Bear, elk, goat, bobcat and deer were all processed, smoked and hung in the smokehouse. When John received a productive yield, brought on by a good day's hunt of grouse, pheasant and prairie chickens, these were also hung in the meat house. The dead birds were hung up by their head in the meat house to add flavor to their meat and to make plucking their feathers much easier. Sometimes John hung them for as long as three weeks before processing them. Each animal or fowl required a different recipe, and John always liked them better when he prepared them in his own special way.

CHAPTER ELEVEN
THE GRIZZLY

John finally became one of the lucky ones in the gold field, but this time it was due to some research and planning before just rushing out into the wilderness and staking a claim. He made some of his money panning gold in the streams, but his big find was from mining in the ground. All he had to do was look for gold instead of coal. It was not easy but John had always been lucky, and the luck of the Irish smiled on him that day. On a little stream and under the biggest boulder in the state of Missouri, John found his gold. Strictly by accident, just visiting an old bear cave, by the little stream and under the boulder that appeared like a mountain, John's luck appeared. John saw the reflecting light from a yellow nugget carefully wedged between some of the crevasses in a rock, purposely left, he knew, by the leprechauns. This reflection was due to his bright miner's lamp, which burned kerosene; and this was not watered down kerosene. John knew from that first nugget that the gold was here and that he had finally found his dream.

John made himself a little lean-to of Western Spruce branches and logs, using a make shift door and a sod with grass roof, to stop the rains and howling wind. Now he could be close to and work this little mine he had dreamed of so many times. He knew from that first day, when he found that first nugget, that he was to be a rich man. All that remained for him was to last out the winter, brave the wilderness, reach Saint Louis and record his claim. Then he would find a buyer, sell the claim and retire a rich man.

One day as John was returning to his lean-to, Thunder was making a lot of unusual and loud noises. Since this was out of the ordinary, he assumed it meant trouble. With Thunder being in the corral and pinned up, John hurried to see what all the commotion and noise was about. When John reached the corral between the mountain and the lean-to, there, between him and Thunder, was the biggest Grizzly bear he had ever seen in this part of the country. The Grizzly was now standing erect on its hind legs, swatting and breaking the rails in the fence like toothpicks. Thunder was running wildly and working himself into a rage. If something were not done soon to rectify the situation, it would mean death for the horse. John was now close enough to detect the foul odor common to the Grizzly Bear. It seemed at this same instant that the bear recognized John's presence and turned to face him. The Grizzly bear has only one enemy and that is man, which he does not encounter very often. When this occurs, it usually ends in death for the bear or man, and sometimes both wind up the victims. Luckily, John remembered to carry Tickler, his fifty-four-caliber rifle, to the mine with him that day. In an instant and without hesitation Tickler spit fire and smoke, sending it's deadly conical bullet to its intended mark. This fast action on John's part saved Thunder's life, and now it was John who needed saving for the great bear was still standing and swaying from side to side. John, thinking quickly, wasted no time in getting to the lean-to for some shelter, and the required time needed to reload Tickler for a second shot. Tickler was only a one shot rifle. Once inside, and with the bear charging blindly toward the lean-to, John somehow managed to remember; the powder first and then the bullet on top of the powder, push it down the barrel with the ramrod, remove the ramrod and add priming powder to the pan. Now, shoot before the bear eats you! BANG went the rifle, with a deafening report from inside the lean-to, just as the bear was

The bear stood tall.

coming through the makeshift door. The lucky shot, as John had no time to aim, was right between the eyes stopping the bear in its tracks. Old timers had always told John not to shoot a Grizzly in the head, as the bullet would not penetrate the thick cellulose bone making up the skull. Some say it would hit and follow the contour of the skull around the head, just giving the bear a huge headache. In this case what else was John to do? First in the door was the mammoth head, and the only shot John had at the time. This could have easily been the end of John and everything around him if it had not been for his reliable rifle, Tickler. From that moment on Tickler was always close at hand for those unexpected encounters in John's daily life on the frontier.

When John skinned that bruin of over eleven feet tall, there was one bullet hole through the heart, which meant the grizzly, was dead on its feet from the first shot. The Grizzly is a fearless beast, scared of absolutely nothing and very difficult to stop with one shot. Having a small brain and a very slow heartbeat, which is an important factor, along with the general health and the size of the bear, makes the time of death, after the vital bullet placement, a scientific guess.

Very seldom does death happen instantly with a Grizzly Bear. Had the second shot from Tickler not been a brain shot, John could have been killed by an already dead bear. John skinned and saved enough bear hide to make two bear skin coats, with the fur attached, two bear skin rugs, a scabbard for Tickler, with enough leftover fur for a windbreaker. There were also several pieces, the size of small blankets, left to make four winter leggings. The leggings were used when walking through deep snow, to wrap John's legs and keep the snow from accumulating in the boots or shoes when wearing snowshoes.

In preparation for storing this much bear meat and to prevent spoilage, John got busy collecting quantities of elderberry bushes and hickory bark. While on previous hunts in the mountains this ancient way of preserving meat was shown to him by the Cheyenne Indians, who were slowly becoming his friends. This concoction of bushes and bark made more smoke than fire when burned wet and provided a slow smoking process, while cooking the meat to a dark, reddish brown. The thick dark crust that formed on the meat helped to keep out insects and rodents, that would have normally devoured the food. This process required a few days of intense smoke and just the right amount of heat and water for the meat to cure properly. This much meat would last a long time and, if some were needed to set the table for relaxed trading, it would be on hand. People become more relaxed on a full stomach, not always caring if the other fellow gets the best deal. In this case, it would be John who was that other fellow.

CHAPTER TWELVE
THE RANCH

As time drifted along, John's bank account was mounting to more than he had ever imagined. He decided to sell his claim to the Saint Louis Mining Company, and take his share yearly for the gold that would be taken out of the mine. Yes, he was going to leave his honeysuckle covered lean-to, which he had turned into quite a nice home in the past two years. He would miss the quiet, winding stream and the mountain background. He would also have to give up his root cellar and his specially built smokehouse. Both of these luxuries were built by his own hands along with everything else he had out here in the wilderness. All of this was tough for John to leave behind, but he was on his way to enjoy life, as he predicted it should be enjoyed, with all its riches. He could not forget his family, whom he not seen for some time. The O'Donnel Mine was to be one of the richest diggings in history and was owned by the Saint Louis Mining Co.

After the fever for gold wore off and John had some time to rest and relax, he decided to try settling down for a while. Now he was going to enjoy the richer life he had always wanted with spices from the Far East and the Orient, and so much exotic food to eat, he would not know where to start. There were many kinds of prepared dishes and for John to correctly pronounce the names of each dish was an impossible task. Many of the dishes, John thought, were superb, and the price was unquestionable, as there was no dish he could not afford. Champagne flowed like water in a babbling brook. John was finally rich and there were no money matters too large for him to handle.

He bought some land for farming, more than he would ever need; all of which was finally turned into the biggest cattle ranch that soon would be known worldwide. Before sending for his family back east, he started a huge log cabin for the main dwelling, a large smokehouse, four root cellars and many outbuildings. Many of these buildings would be required for the help it would take to manage such a spread. Long before the family's arrival, the main house and most of the barns were finished.

There were also line shacks built in the higher elevations. Each was equipped with beds and a stove for warmth as well as cooking, and could be used by anyone, not just the ranch hands. If someone was passing through and needed a place to bunk for the night this was an accepted hospitality on the open range. Sleeping under the stars in the higher elevations in late spring and early summer still felt pretty cold even to the tough and rugged cowboys. The Ranch was now ready for the cattle coming from the East.

Water on this particular ranch was not difficult to find, as the water table was very high and located just under the ground. There were also many lakes throughout the range area. This made it easy to feed grain and hay anywhere along the way to the cattle during the winter months. Also not having to haul the water by wagon all over the ranch was less of a burden to the cowboys and the ranch hands. The cattle were moved to higher elevations during late spring and summer getting fat and healthy grazing on the thick sweet grasslands east of the river.

Getting his family to Missouri required the help of a wagon train and the railroad to bring all the people he had sent to escort his family and assure their safe arrival from back east. The way people functioned, lived and survived out west was an exciting new experience for his family. Where they were going to be living and working was in a totally new untamed territory to them and everyone else. No, this life was not going to be a piece of cake, but they would easily endure it because of the past hardships they had been forced to undertake for so long. This was also receiving a new chance in life, because everything was different, and it became a learning experience as well as a job.

John's money, that he would give to his family to maintain the ranch and live a new way of life, would also lessen many of the burdens they would encounter during this breaking-in period. His family, not being accustomed to having money, required an adjustment period. They did not know how much money John was worth at the time, and John was not sure either. What he did know was that he didn't have to ask the cost of his purchases. When he purchased an item, regardless of the cost, the Mining Company paid for it, and there were no questions asked.

John's family would take this ranch to great heights of fame by making it world renowned with their high quality line of beef and breeding stock. Unheard of in the west or anywhere else, these Longhorns, as they were called, had bloodlines dating back to the time when cattle were introduced to this world through the great explorer Cortez, from Spain and Mexico. These bloodlines had been in existence for thousands of years and were now being mixed with cattle from the Far East. There was a lot of time and toil, trial and error before the great line was established. Every farmer in the United States and the Territories was trying to get this string of cattle, which was started at the O'Donnel Ranch. Every rancher wanted fifteen cows and one bull, to start his own herd. Great herds were, indeed, started and they flourished throughout the country, spreading and extending this unique breed far and wide.

LONGHORN BULL

CHAPTER THIRTEEN
BLUE SKY

John could not understand why, but little more than a year passed since the arrival of his family, when that ghostly calling returned, that part of him that was saying, "I need to go ride on the wild side." He gave the ranch to his family and was heading out to… he didn't know. With Thunder under him, a bedroll on his saddle, a canteen on the saddle horn and Tickler securely tucked in his scabbard; he was back on a journey that only he could ride. He was destined to become a trapper and later a fur trader. John became very skilled in trapping and through trial and error he quickly learned about the animals that were out in the wild and their habits, making it much easier to take their hides. Having many nice prime pelts made trading easier with the Indians in this area. John quickly realized, in most cases, the Indians were receiving the best deal. He learned many new ideas and skills from them and put them to good use. He was definitely learning a new way of life and a survival process unknown to him until now.

Even though John hadn't seen a white man in a year and a half, time was quickly passing by. He seemed not to miss having a companion, although someone to converse with about the day's events, over the burning embers of the fire before retiring for the night would have made the evenings and days pass more pleasantly.

As John picked up this new way of life the Indians were becoming his friends. He often spent time in their camps and villages, learning their ways, while trading skins and meat for clothes and other gear, which were necessary to have, while out in the wilderness.

He was a well-seasoned and experienced Mountain Man by the time he entered the Cheyenne village. Mastering their language very easily and accepting the Indian way of life made his acceptance into the tribe inevitable. John was the Cheyenne's friend (translated to their language, "hi viss ssi ni"). This was an honor not given to every white man (vi' ho l) and one he would always treasure in his heart. When the next tribal meeting was held, John was already their blood brother (ni hi ni hin o zi) and was welcomed throughout the tribal nation, wherever a Cheyenne campfire burned or a teepee was erected.

One day a Cougar attacked one of the younger boys who had gone berry hunting. John, hearing the loud noises as the Indians returned to the village, saw the injured boy. The boy was terror-stricken. The Cougar's teeth and claws had ripped some nasty gashes in his side. After seeing the boy's cut and gnawed body, John was automatically guided to his saddlebag. After retrieving his needle and thread, he proceeded to sew and close up the boy's gashes. This was not a new or unusual sight to him because he had seen this done in the mines many times, not from Cougars, but after cave-ins or an early blast of dynamite. Time passed and John thought no more about the incident. The boy quickly recovered. John was astonished when one day the boy's father entered his teepee. He brought with him his daughter, who was nineteen years of age, and told John that for returning his son to him, he was giving him his daughter in marriage. This was an honor he could not turn down. It would bring disgrace to the girl and to the tribe if he were to refuse. John had no desire to disgrace the girl or to start an Indian uprising. Besides, she was very pretty and he needed a traveling companion. John did the only respectable thing he could do and agreed to accept her hand in marriage. Her name was Tseotatavo, meaning Blue Sky.

One day John sat by the little mountain stream as it wound and twisted back and forth through the rocks and trees, finally reaching the plush green valley between the monstrous mountains he loved so dearly. His thoughts were of his beautiful new bride-to-be, as the wedding ceremony was quickly approaching, not leaving much time for a decision to be made about an appropriate wedding present for him to present to her on this special occasion. After giving the idea considerable thought and weighing many factors, John decided to make her a saddle. The saddle would be made from crimson colored saddle leather, a full quarter inch thick. This would require many hard hours of tooling the leather and putting the finishing touches on the petite seat of leather before the finished product would be cinched down on her chestnut colored Indian pony. To compare her miniature petite pony to his magnificent stallion Thunder, was a funny thought, however, the two looked as if, somehow, they belonged together. The small frame and petite body of thirteen and a half hands, compared to seventeen hands and rippling muscles, and one and a half times the width and length in body of

Thunder was a considerable difference. When he thought about the size difference between himself and Blue Sky, a different light was shed on the subject and he quickly accepted the difference, and didn't really understand why there had been any thought on the subject. The prospect of being together for an eternity had not really taken hold. It would take awhile for all of this to make sense and a meaning to form.

John not only made her a new saddle with silver conches all the way around the skirt of the saddle, but also added a new combined rawhide and horsehair lariat. For the lariat to be properly finished, he took hair from both of the horse's tails and made a beautiful and strong lasso. The leather designed with the two different color tail hairs had a striking appearance. While John was working on the lariat his thoughts wandered to Tseotatavo's beautiful soft black hair, below her waist in length. He was thinking, if he explained how much the use of the hair would mean to him and how it would help tie the bond between them… well, at least he thought it was a good idea. A better idea came to him when he decided not to pursue the issue. His thoughts may have not been taken or received warmly, especially when he would have asked for her hair, for a lasso. This was perhaps not the proper question, or the right way to begin a long marriage. Perhaps the gift of a different lasso and many moons passing would make a difference for this difficult question and make it seem not so ridiculously stupid to ask. Perhaps not! Chances are the answer would remain the same.

Marriage was exactly what John needed in life. It cured his rambling around alone. Now he had someone to ramble with, and ramble they did. John and Blue Sky never returned to his ranch or to the village where she had become his bride.

There was something deep inside both of them, a calling of the wild, to see what was on the other side of the mountain and over the next horizon. When a house appeared in the distance, it was time to pack up the teepee and head for taller timber, as civilization was not far behind. First came the trapper with a simple lean-to, then a house, next a settlement; slowly a town would evolve, finally growing into a city. Civilization was everywhere and growing like a wild fire in sagebrush, already covering the prairie, with towns popping up overnight, and now it was heading for the mountains.

John and Blue Sky welcomed all adventures, meeting every challenge head on, always learning something for the next adventure they would face. Even when they were not seeking excitement and adventure, it became inevitable that a challenge would present itself to these two every day.

On one occasion while simply gathering firewood, a lovers duel between these two arose, to see who could gather the most firewood in the least amount of time. Before either of these two would give up and admit the other had won, they had gathered enough wood for the whole Cheyenne Nation to use for many winters to come.

Time was moving faster than ever, and John was still moon struck over Blue Sky. He was trying to accept and thoroughly understand all of the new happenings that were going on around him. He enjoyed seeing and doing everything with his loving bride and partner. He never imagined life could be this much fun. He was really trying hard not to forget anything, but with everything happening so quickly, he completely forgot about winter approaching. Blue Sky was not only going to do the fun things. She deserved the credit for returning John to reality. Together they quickly set up camp and made their preparations for the winter snows that would cascade the mountains, making travel almost impossible. Snowshoes were about the only way to get around, as the snow was just too deep to wade through and they needed to walk on top of the snow. John and Blue Sky carefully planned their first winter's stay together, in their own Teepee. With the combined knowledge of survival they had acquired in the wilderness and their many other skills, they were able to successfully brave the blizzards and attend that last Rendezvous of Mountain Men in the spring.

CHAPTER FOURTEEN
THE GATHERING

Yes, John and Blue Sky were there for the last Rendezvous. The last stand of the Mountain Man was something that would require much planning and something they knew they could not miss. The period recognized an era in time, with the gathering of Mountain Men and Indians, uniting for one last big party, which marked the end of the Mountain Man era. This was a time that was and would be, important to history. This gathering would be responsible for many changes, creating a unity of all breeds, before civilization, moving swiftly, engulfed the nation. The Mountain Man and the Indian, now working and sometimes living together, were at the peak of their domain. The greatest feast and reunion ever held in the west was about to begin, where black, red and white or whatever color men were to join together and celebrate one of the greatest and historic moments in history.

This was a word-of-mouth event that had been spread throughout many states and territories. Any time people met, even strangers, the Rendezvous was spoken about. The exact location and the exact date would be worked out in the future, but, "if you're going to be in the general area, well, plan on stopping by and check it out." They did know the date was set for the spring of eighteen hundred forty and the event was to be held somewhere close to Saint Louis. This many people together, in one area, required plenty of space, and a huge arena. Where the first group of people gathered was an appropriate location and appeared to be as good a place as any. Since they were the first group to arrive, it only seemed natural that they would be chosen to establish a place to hold the event.

This unforgettable event took place on the open plains where the river bends sharply to the south, just three miles southeast of Saint Louis, Missouri. The river being close for access to plenty of water made this an ideal location. There were also plenty of hardwood trees for firewood that extended all the way to the mountains. The only requirement was to cut the firewood or dip the water and haul it to camp. Immediately some of the Mountain Men elected a firewood chopping committee and used one of the wagons daily for firewood and water. This gave everyone more time for enjoying their beautiful surroundings and spending more time telling yarns, or exaggerating stories. By the time this shindig was over, the town had expanded outward nearly three miles, without having to cut or clear a tree.

It was here, during the last Rendezvous, that not only the famous but also some of the infamous Indians and the Mountain Men of the past and present were recognized. Everyone received honored praise and position for their courageous and innovative deeds and performance in those changing times. Legends were told and learned, then retold and spread from camp to camp, not only at this gathering but also at many gatherings to come. The Great Spirits knew that with this gathering many issues would be settled, after being brought to the proper attention of others and released to new heights. The wisdom and knowledge that was taught would expand throughout the lands so that everyone could, in their own way, accept what they wanted to believe as truth.

Travelers to this event used all known transportation means possible: horses; boats; horse drawn wagons, mules; goat carts, railroad, foot travel and even some came on bicycles. Many people hauled their tents and teepees, poles for lean-tos and the like, in all kinds of fashion. Some shouldered their makeshift homes, while others dragged them behind horses and oxen. When available, many used wagons to haul the abundance of poles required for teepees and lean-tos. Their main objective was to have a good time, enjoy themselves and be as laid-back and comfortable as possible without worry and grief. Right or wrong, this was a time for everyone young or old, to stand up and be counted. Let those be recognized for who they are, and not for who they would later become.

The food was in abundance. If it grew, it was eaten, from varmint to Grizzly Bear. Every concoction imaginable was on exhibit, every teepee and camp trying to out do the next. Teepees and camps stretched as far as the eye could see and beyond. This was a trader's paradise. Hand made items of every description, every trinket and ornament known to man, were on display in one area.

Everyone was dressed in his or her best attire for this memorable occasion. Words cannot describe the colorful outfits. Indians were in their full dress war bonnets and Mountain Men in their buckskins with all the trimmings. The women and the men participating in this last Rendezvous made many of the garments worn at this event. Women wore white deer skin dresses, as white as the fresh fallen snow, many decorated with elaborate bead works of various designs, some taking months to make. The Indian women always dressed their men with the best clothing available, whether it was manufactured by weaving the material together, or from the skins and pelts of the local animals. They also used many different designs and bright dyes; they tried to make one outfit stand out above the others. While they could only make and accomplish so much with the equipment and supplies they had on hand, what they accomplished was incredible.

The Indians and the Mountain Men were from a proud clan of people. They were especially proud of themselves, their achievements and their possessions. The Rendezvous gave them an opportunity to shine and show off to each other. This was an event they could share peacefully while having a wonderful time. Competition became a very important peaceful way to solve disagreements and to show the best competitor at a given sport at any given time. There was always some kind of competition to enter. Games of skill and chance were set up throughout the area. Just watching without being a competitor taught and gave onlookers the appreciation for many of the sports that were previously unheard of or taken for granted.

Tomahawk and knife throwing were two of the main events held daily in all the camp areas. One of the rules when throwing the knife or the tomahawk was to have at least one revolution of the blade for every twelve feet before sticking the target. When a knife was held and thrown by the handle, a complete spin or turn was required. When throwing the knife by holding the blade, at least a turn and a half was required for the blade to wind up, point first, into the target. These rules stopped the competitors from throwing the knife or the tomahawk like a dart. The knives and the tomahawks often weighed more than a pound and to throw accurately required a steady aim. A competitor also needed a lot of strength in the forearm and the shoulder to throw the necessary distance, and to maintain accuracy. Some of these targets required much more skill than others. Sometimes strings were hung in front of a target and the competitor was required to cut the string as well as hit the target. Often the target would be a swinging block of wood, hung from a rope that would be released as each competitor toed the line. The line or the required distance to the target often varied, but was seldom less than twelve feet.

JOHN'S TOMAHAWK

One of the easiest competitions to judge was to give each competitor five throws at a playing card stuck flat on a block of wood. The card being stuck without the knife coming outside the playing card edge counted five points. If the card was stuck with the knife blade protruding out of the edge of the card, it counted three points and when only the block was stuck, missing the card entirely, it counted as one point. An excellent and top score would have been twenty-five points for five throws, a feat not readily accomplished by most competitors. The tomahawk scoring was almost the same, using five throws, except that a card cut entirely in half counted as five points. When squirrel hunting with a tomahawk, many times the hunter would wind up with two pieces of squirrel when a direct hit was achieved. This was referred to as the center cut throw.

CHAPTER FIFTEEN
THE KNIFE

While John was a still a blacksmith's apprentice he had the opportunity to meet Mr. Jim Bowie. This event took place in May of Eighteen hundred thirty five, which was less than a year before Jim's untimely death, at the battle of the Alamo. Jim was returning from the San Saba mines, which were loaded with silver and gold. These mines were later known as the Bowie mines, which were located near the geographic center of Texas.

The way they met was strictly by accident, as John had overheard the local people in town saying that Mr. Jim Bowie was on a business trip to see one of the mining companies in St.Louis. He was on his way to town that very week to draw up a deal and get it finalized before his journey back to Texas. Mr. Bowie's name was well known and, if he were coming through Missouri into Saint Louis to close an important deal, everyone would know when and where the closing would be held. Since John just happened to be in town at the same time, and with Mr. Bowie's fame, John just had to meet him. With very little introduction, as it turned out, with the luck of the Irish, they became friends right off. It seemed they had much in common and believed in the same things for mankind and humanity.

Even though Bowie was born in Kentucky in Seventeen ninety-six, he moved with his family to Missouri and then to Louisiana at an early age. Bowie talked about the move as if he remembered every mile, and he may well have. Sometimes as an adult, when remembering things that happened as a child, the memories become very clear in the mind, but if things are a little blurry, it is always possible to ad-lib. Jim had his already famous Bowie knife, which was made famous by him in a bloody battle on a sandbar, where he was also badly wounded, in Eighteen twenty-seven near Natchez, Mississippi. The famous Bowie Knife was really designed by Jim's brother, Rezin Bowie, and the actual knife was made by Rezin's blacksmith, Jesse Clift, in the Parish of Avoyelles, located in Central Louisiana. It was after Jim used it as a weapon on that sandbar to defend himself, that the knife became famous. Perhaps it was really Jim who became famous by the way he defended himself and the knife just happened to be there for the using.

John quickly saw the need for the use of such a knife in the wilderness and did not forget about the idea. After much trial and error, John designed a knife at the blacksmith shop. The unique design was a cross between the Arkansas Toothpick and the Bowie. He found out that making his knife from the Damascus steel, for strength, pliability and the sharpness of a razor, was a slow tedious process, but definitely worth the effort. John did not finish the knife while he was working in the blacksmith shop.

Located in the state of Texas, the Alamo fell after two thousand Mexicans stormed the walls and gates for a thirteen-day period. On March the sixth, Eighteen thirty-six at six thirty in the morning; the firing from the fort had stopped. One hundred and eighty nine Heroes had offered their lives to insure the freedom of Texas. James Bowie, age 41, and David (Davy) Crockett, age 50, were among those Heroes. The Mexican General Santa Anna, disguised as a peasant, was captured the following day. The independence of Texas was won!

When John realized the last Rendezvous date was quickly approaching and that it was to be held in Saint Louis, his thoughts were to finish the knife for this special occasion. This way he could pay tribute to Mr. Bowie's knife and at the same time, sort of pay a tribute to Jim. It would also give him a chance to show off some of the fancy blacksmith work he had learned. A few years had passed since he had worked on this project. He did not want to drum up any new business, but he did enjoy the feel of the hammer hitting and pounding against the steel. He also enjoyed watching the finished product mold into its finished state against his anvil. He could give the project as much detail as he needed or wanted. Time was not a factor, as he was actually creating the mold. It was his project and he would finish it at the right time.

What he accomplished was making a knife with a fourteen-inch long blade, one and three quarters inch wide and a full quarter inch thick. This knife could easily be used for cutting kindling for the fire, as it actually resembled a small sword. A knife of this size was not to be used for the small camp chores or skinning small game, but it was handy to have around. In the event of an emergency, such as taking on a bear, when Tickler was not at hand, using his knife certainly would not have been unheard of, or an unusual choice of weapons for the chore.

His design was like a dagger with both edges sharp as a razor, allowing it to slip into its intended target like a hot knife cutting butter. John put buffalo horn on both sides above the hilt of the knife and carefully attached it with silver pins. After casting the thumb and finger guard out of silver and adding some fancy tooling, the knife was casting a new light and becoming very impressive, making his hard work and efforts worthwhile. The buffalo horn made a sturdy and dependable handle, which would outlast the normal life span of any knife and the silver gave it that added touch of perfection. The finished product weighed approximately one and three quarter pounds.

JOHN'S DAMASCUS KNIFE

CHAPTER SIXTEEN
THE TEEPEE

One morning about a month before the Rendezvous as Blue Sky awoke, the sun was finding its way through the teepee door and creeping toward her bed roll of warm bear skins and mink. The morning sunshine was brightening the teepee floor and she had a feeling she was not alone any longer. After calling for John several times then remembering he had gotten up earlier to go fishing at the nearby creek, she eased the blanket back over the bearskins. No, she was not alone, for there next to her was a big, long, black and red Diamond Back Rattlesnake. Obviously the snake had crawled through the opening in the teepee looking for shelter from the cold outside and had found a warm place to stay beside Blue Sky. Blue Sky immediately decided the snake would not make a good sleeping partner. She quickly jumped from under her bed covers before the snake could strike and deposit its deadly venom. Perhaps the snake would not have bitten her, but she was not taking any chances, as she really was not a lover of snakes.

When John returned with several nice small Brown Trout from the stream, Blue Sky already had the rattlesnake cooking for breakfast. After telling John of her experience they searched everything inside the Teepee making sure that was the only intruder they would encounter. After setting their minds at ease, Blue Sky prepared the snakeskin for the tanning process. John and Blue Sky decided to keep the door tied shut and make adjustments for additional morning air with the flaps located at the top of the teepee.

Blue Sky was constantly making things for John and this time she made him a beautiful hand tooled leather knife case, made just for this special occasion, the Rendezvous. She sewed the case from the soft tanned black deer hide that she had processed and spent most of the winter chewing on to give it flexibility. The case easily slipped into John's woven woolen red and black sash, which she had also made with the matching leg ties to keep the briars out of the tops of his deer hide moccasins. Today at the Rendezvous, John was also wearing his brand new broad brim hat, with the shiny rattlesnake hatband that Blue Sky tanned for him. One might say," He was rather decked out for the occasion and having a wonderful time."

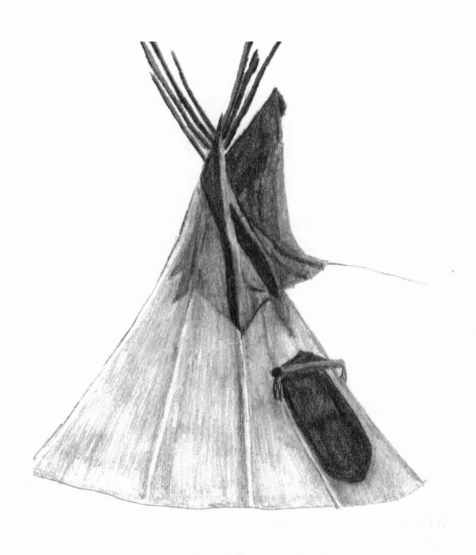

JOHN AND BLUESKY'S TEEPEE

CHAPTER SEVENTEEN
GAMES AND FUN

John won many of the competitions that he entered with ease. Experience with many encounters throughout his life as a child, miner, blacksmith, carpenter and now a Mountain Man had allowed him to actually become experienced at many of the events he was trying to win without really practicing.

Many of the things he had learned through life were actually helping him to win the events that were happening around him.

For instance, John knew little of the tomahawk until he actually lived with the Indians. While living there, he also became familiar with the Squaw Axe, as it was sometimes called. This little axe had a blade on one side, with the other side usually dubbed down flat so one could use the tomahawk for pounding, much like a hammer. At first John confused the name, Squaw Axe with the pipe for smoking, known as the peace pipe, but they were used for two different purposes. Although the Squaw might be able to make peace with her axe, if she were forced to go on the warpath. John sometimes wondered why it was called a peace pipe, as it was smoked at all rituals before war or after. Sometimes he thought they just needed an excuse to smoke the tobacco for a recreational past time or what ever else was being smoked at the gathering. The throwing of the tomahawk originally was designed to be a game for the children to play and a way for them to gain confidence while acquiring weapons skills for future use. Many times the actual war tomahawk had a spike on one side and a blade on the other, definitely a utensil used for destruction, and hardly necessary at the Sunday social. When at war, if a warrior threw the only weapon he had, it had better stick, and stop its intended victim or he became the victim. The tomahawk is a vicious weapon whether thrown or held in ones hand and used for self-defense. John spent many long hours perfecting the sport of sticking his target while hoping his expertise and efforts would not have to be used in war. As a result, he mastered most of the techniques of throwing. There was the overhand throw that was released something like a baseball. The underhand throw, although not a powerful throw, could be used in the underbrush or when overhead predators and obstacles were present. The side arm throw was much like the overhand release, only delivered with a sidearm swing. The rabbit throw was not necessarily the last one to be used, but it is the last one mentioned here and is one of the hardest to learn to stick because of judging the distance. The rabbit throw allowed the handle to be straight up in the air, with the blade close to the ground upon reaching its intended target. This was a very important position of the handle, especially if one wanted to eat rabbit. To propel this awkward instrument through the air and hit his intended target required many hours of repetitious practice and concentration with a skilled delivery from the hand and arm. When the tomahawk was thrown properly, but the distance was improperly calculated it caused the handle to point down towards the ground upon reaching the intended target. The handle would hit the ground and bounce over the rabbit. When the distance was accurately calculated and the handle was pointing straight up in the air on contact with the rabbit or its intended target, the blade was allowed to do its intended job. To hit a running rabbit John needed to be fast and accurate, with a true aim. A feat of obtaining the running rabbit came with many hours of intense practice and luck.

John and Tickler fit right into the competitions. Not only was John skilled with his knife and tomahawk but also everything going on around the camps was catered to John's life. It was almost as if this party were being held just for him.

John had not really done much competitive shooting, but he had done a lot of shooting; and over years of much practice and patience, John acquired quite a skill with the rifle and pistol. He did not rely on his pistol for hunting purposes, even though he could handle one very skillfully and accurately. One of his justifications for using the pistol was that, it was a firearm that was light to carry, and would only be used for personal protection. Also, he did not believe the pistol had enough energy or hitting and stopping power to be a reliable hunting weapon. The main reason this was not a practical hunting piece was the reduced length of the barrel. The barrel was too short to burn the required amount of powder to give power and to propel the bullet. The main objective and reason for self-protection during this era was to keep someone or something from maiming you. Sometimes for the thief or mugger to know that John carried a pistol was all that was needed for his safety. The question about whether or not he could use it never came up. Just to have it for display was all that was usually required.

Shooting at any gathering always ran a close second place to any other competition or event, often rating number one in the opinion of many minds. There were many competitors shooting for the mark or target. Usually an X was carved in the end of a log or etched with a piece of charcoal. The skilled individual, who placed the bullet closest to the center of the mark, would win that particular round. Just winning once did not make them the best at the sport; there was always someone else to challenge that position. Many times the challengers were the same people from the last round of competition. Everyone wanted to be a winner, if only to say they had won once by being closest to the center of the mark. Sometimes a wager was required to compete in the competition. The wager was generally small, decided and agreed upon by the competitors before the competition started. To enter the event could require a squirrel or rabbit pelt, lead, powder, a chew of tobacco, perhaps a drink of liquor or some smoking tobacco. The winner would receive all the wagers for that round of competition. Sometimes they threw and shot for the sport of it and did not compete. This was a way of passing time while getting acquainted with one another.

Of course, there were the typical games sometimes played for competition but mainly played just for fun. The three-legged race, sack race and the wheelbarrow relay, were some of the best known games, common to this day. These games were played and enjoyed by many participants of all ages. The rules for those not familiar with the three-legged race go as follows: two people as partners stand side by side, facing in the same direction and tie their two touching legs together. Then the object of the game is to reach a preset marked distance, before their opponents. This is a skill that requires fast walking and running together while staying in rhythm with each other. If one maintained one's balance and kept from falling, he could avoid bringing his or her partner to the ground.

The typical sack race is achieved by putting both feet into a sack, pulling up the sack at least to the waist, tying the sack securely around the waist, and jumping to a marked distance before the opponents. Keeping one's balance while jumping with both feet together is hard to do and becomes quite a task. Running, which requires one type of balance and coordination, is not the same type required for jumping fast. To achieve a win requires more coordination and skill than is

JOHN AND BLUESKY AT THE
RENDEZVOUS

normally used in a regular day's activity, causing physical strain and stress on body parts. John found that he and Blue Sky didn't notice any change until the next day when they were resting and found out they couldn't move any of their body parts without a lot of pain, especially in the joints and muscles. This was not necessarily from using them too much, but more than likely from falling on them numerous times throughout the events. John noted that the reactions from the competitors of the three-legged race by being tied together with Blue Sky and the sack race with jumping and always loosing their balance caused much laughter from the non-competitors. With this much fun even the loser didn't feel so bad. There were just two competitors in one sack race, so there could only be one winner and one loser. Rather than calling the other person a loser, the judge of the event told the non-winner that he was in second place, a much nicer way than saying he lost the race. Coming in second place could even give him bragging rights.

The wheelbarrow relay was Johns and Blue Sky's favorite race. This requires one person to lie face down on the ground, while the other person in a standing position, aligns themselves between the legs of the person on the ground. The person standing up, then bends over and picks up the legs of the person on the ground and holds them tightly around his or her waist. The person on the ground uses their hands and arms like legs, moving forward very fast, to the finish line or the halfway mark. Once at the half way mark they would change positions with their partner and, moving as fast as possible try to return back to the starting point before their opponents, and win the race. With John's massive build and Blue Sky's rather small frame, it was very easy for John to pick her up, holding her legs around his waist. This way it just looked as though she was using her arms and hands. When it was John's turn on the ground, all Blue Sky had to do was hold his legs around her tiny waist and point him in the direction of the finish line. Once they were pointed in the right direction, with the strength in his massive arms and shoulders, he would pull both of them over the finish line for an easy win.

New techniques of horseback riding, all the fancy tricks of mounting and dismounting with the horse running at a full gallop, were always in demand and appreciated. These popular feats for competition were tried and retried until a winner was chosen. John and Blue Sky watched with astonishment as a horse moved backwards almost as fast as he moved forwards, shifting from side to side with ease, his rider sitting straight in the saddle, as though nothing out of the ordinary was happening.

Talented roping skills were well worth watching and always being demonstrated throughout the various camps. Choosing the best event for just one day was impossible, as each one had its own unique ways and techniques. An idle moment was unheard of, especially in a place with this many people as spectators, who always required something new to be seen or done. Just as one event finished, another got started. No one was willing to let these wonderful moments in time to come to an end without recognition for everyone. Young and old alike took part in everything from eating and telling stories to playing games and entering competitions; no one was left out. Each and every person participated by sharing his or her thoughts and stories at this wonderful gathering.

No one knows for sure how much actual time this event took. There are no positive accounts on record of the actual time spent or how many moons passed before this great party ended. The endless planning for the future and all the accomplishments made during this short period of time can only be imagined in one's mind. Whether it took days, weeks or months is irrelevant. Red men and white men were together, in the same arena, without a fierce blood letting battle. They were spinning yarns and telling tales of the past and predicting the future. Papoose and paleface children would cherish these moments in their hearts and relive these stories forever. Over and over these stories would be told to their children and their children's children for years to come. These tales about the simple events that were shared by everyone at the last Rendezvous would be responsible for warming many teepees and cabins throughout history. What a story-telling time this turned out to be!

EPILOGUE

John and Tseotatavo never returned to the East and never became rich with money. What they had, no money could buy for they were happy with everything they ever wanted at their fingertips. Love, health and happiness are three important factors to be considered in any relationship, especially in a bonding marriage like these two people were sharing with one another, everlasting and non-separable from each other throughout their lives.

John and Blue Sky became part of nature and accepted life as it should be lived, free of worry with the right to explore and move on to new adventures. Nature was running her course with Blue Sky and John as Her partners throughout eternity.

AUTHOR'S PHILOSOPHY

If life were only that simple today! Wait a minute. Is it possible we are missing something? Do we need to move west and find our fortune like John? Is it possible that his riches were the joys and understanding he had obtained through the experiences of life, only to be known to those who search with an open mind and heart seeking new experiences? Lean not necessarily to the four winds for the answers, but to the realism and the adventures encountered in your life at hand.

7 July 2023

MAY YOUR PLEASURES
BE MANY AND YOUR
TROUBLES BE
FEW

Charles Brightin